The Sun & the Moon Stood Still

Gina Woo

ISBN (ebook) 978-1-951191-047

ISBN (paperback) 978-1-951191-054

Published by Of Ink & Pearls Publishing.

Cover by JD Cover Designs.

Formatting by Lindsey Teske.

Formatting by Sharmin Sultana.

Dedication

To Gordon, who has been listening to my poetry for years.

Preface

I was hit by a car when I was a young girl. My parents were told that I would probably die.

My mother and I went to an Assembly of God Church, but my dad would not go to church. He would not let my mom or myself speak to him about the Lord. My mom went to church every week.

After the accident, the church prayed for the Lord to heal me. They prayed for 2 months while I lay in a coma.

During that time, the most important thing in my mind was whether my dad had become a true Christian yet.

While I was still in the coma, I asked him, "Dad, are you a Christian yet?"

He said, "I don't know what a true Christian is."

I said, "It's a person who loves God and wants to serve Him."

He didn't answer me, but that night he told my mom, "If Gina is ever able to walk into church again, I will go too."

As the church prayed for me each week, I slowly came out of my coma and began to heal. They prayed for me to walk, and I could stand in my father's arms. They prayed for me to talk and I said my sister's name.

When I was able to walk again my dad came to church with me. Since he had a hardened heart toward the Lord, it took many months, but he finally accepted Jesus as his Saviour.

Table Of Contents

That's Love

I love to read the Bible,
For it is all so true.

For in the Holy Scriptures
It possesses life for you.

It only takes a second
For Christ, your life to renew.

If you would only ask Him
This miracle to do.

Take away my sins and forgive.
Come into my heart to live.

Then all these things, mentioned above,
Can be yours just by asking.

That's Love.

Genesis

God made the sun to shine far,
That provide so much light.
God made the many stars,
To shine over the land at night.

God made the waters to swish,
And the great many whales.
God made all the fish,
Through the water they sail.

Noah was given plans to follow,
And he built a big boat.
Inside there was room it was hollow,
For all the animals, that it would float.

A zebra, a tiger, a lion and bear,
Two by two up the ramp they went.
Sturdy it was, to walk with care,
Some of the animals did make a dent.

It rained for 40 days and nights,
On a mountain the Ark did rest.
A raven was sent to find light,
To see if she could find her nest.

She found no place to land,
She had to return to the Ark.
Not even a tree was on hand,
For her to land on its bark.

Later Noah sent forth a dove bringing
Food, to see if she could find land.
She flew away singing,
And later was seen walking on sand.

Exodus

I know that my life will always be,
Dedicated to my God.
He has performed many miracles in my life,
Like the one concerning the rod.

One day God said to Moses,
"Lead my people out of this land."
Moses said, "But the people will not believe me,"
God said, "What is that in your hand?"

Moses said, "A rod,"
God said, "Throw it on the ground."
And when he did just that,
To his surprise he found

That it became a serpent.
He could do many miracles with the rod.
Not because of his own magic,
But because of the power of God.

So you can see why I serve God,
Because I love Him dearly.
Because He died for me,
And when He did, He set me free.

Year of the Jubilee

Year by year I work so hard,
Pressing bricks together along with the tar.
Maybe soon we'll be finished with this yard,
Going to the next one that isn't very far.

Day by day the sun gets so hot,
Walking in my sandals my feet with mud collide.
When the day is done and the race I have fought,
On the way home I'll have a donkey's ride.

I've been working many days and have more to go,
Till I hear the Master calling me to Him.
Come now take a rest from all that you sow,
This is Jubilee and I want you to rest your limb.

When that day is here and I know it's coming fast,
I will celebrate and jump for joy!
I will begin to say I will be home at last!

Moses

Many years I've been leading Israel,
Through the Wilderness and the barren land.
I listen to His voice,
And He tells me I'm following his plan.

The Lord is leading them from Egypt,
He wants them to trust Him and Obey.
He said, "Moses, I want you to be their leader,
Because I want Israel to follow my way."

Sometimes, when they've been thirsty,
And there is nothing to drink.
I wish I was near my house,
So I can get water from my sink.

Instead I hear them complaining,
Where shall we get water today?
There is no food or figs or Vines,
And we are not even near a bay.

So I told Moses to speak to the Rock,
That water from it would spring.
So he went to the stone out yonder,
And a rod with him he did bring.

Saying, "So water is what you want,
So you won't die out here!"
He hit the rod on the rock,
The water came out very clear.

We should learn to trust the Lord,
In all we say and do.
Then tomorrow we won't worry,
If we learn to trust in You.

Deuteronomy

Through the mountains the wind has gone,
Camels roam through the desert land.
You can see what the Lord has done,
Just by the moving of His mighty hand.

As an eagle is an example to her young,
By flying around her nest.
She hopes the song she has sung,
Will encourage them to fly to the West.

When she has sung to the right chord,
She spreads her wings out yonder.
When they climb on board,
She'll take them for a ride out wander.

This is much like the Lord teaches you,
When He thinks it's time to fly.
He shows you what He'd like you to do
And gives you a vision for a sign.

He always gives us a choice,

He leads us as we go.

If we listen to His voice,

A bountiful harvest we will sow.

Joshua

Be strong and courageous, Joshua,
For I am leading you.
As Moses trusted me,
You must give Me your hand too.

When you come to the River Jordan,
And it looks so big and large.
I know you must be thinking,
I should have brought my barge.

The ark shall go before you,
Remember the Covenant we made?
If your faith in Me you'll keep,
You'll see the water stand in a heap.

Onward to the city of Jericho,
I want you to march around this land.
On the seventh day when you march,
The walls will fall like sand.

Joshua captured many cities,
With the Lord's help many times.
He even causes the sun to stand still,
Right in the middle for a sign.

The Lord has helped us,
In so many ways.
Who will you serve
In all of your days?

Judges

In foreign lands, Israel went after other gods,
Worked in cities they were in.
Dwelt among people whose customs were odd,
God sent people to deliver them from sin.

Debra from Bethel was under a palm tree.
She watched the people as they would come,
For advice on a problem and a way to agree,
Sisera will be defeated by a mom.

I will go with you, Barak, of course,
As you take men of war to fight him.
But victory in battle will not be yours,
The sun on the battle will be dim.

For you have not trusted the Lord,
Hearing rumors, you're fearing very much.
As we go and take our sword,
You will know I have the Lord's touch.

They went to the plain of Kedesh,
Pursuing after Sisera with chariots.
The horses traveled so fast,
While running and jumping over pits.

Jael went out to Sisera and said, "Hi,
Come inside my place for a rest.
Wait till the army goes by,
They are going farther to the west."

Jael took a nail she found nearby,
Hammered it straight into his head.
She found and showed Barak the guy
That you're looking for, and he is now dead.

Ruth

As He laid His hand on me,
While working in the fields today.
I could hear Him softly say,
"Trust in Me and I'll lead the way."

As I turned the tractor to the right,
I looked and saw the Big Sky.
There was the sun shining bright,
Over the hills and mountains so high.

I thought how beautiful Heaven must be,
Where the Son of Man lives this day.
Is He taking me through these fields,
To show me His better way?

There are fields of people who need to hear
The way and all the truth.
If leaving this farm is what You want,
Then I will be like Ruth.

And glean in the field you have for me,
Where the lost are waiting to hear.
And I will stay here on my knee,
To know if the fields are far or near.

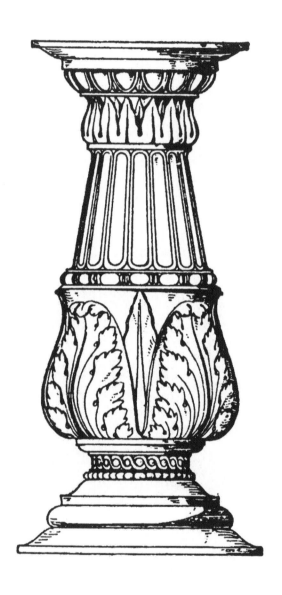

Samuel

Helping daily with many tasks,
Samuel grew up in the house of the Lord.
Dusting, cleaning, doing what they ask,
And studying the Holy Word.

"Eli, I miss my mom and dad,
Are they coming for a visit soon?"
"My child, why is your face so sad?
Won't you join me in singing this tune?"

I'll play the cymbals, you play bass.
We can dance around the room.
Just don't hit the flower vase,
I don't want to have to use the broom.

Then we'll take a camel ride,
Up the hill and down.
Those camels need to move to the other side,
Just west of the little town.

Next, we'll study the Torah today,
We'll read about the Exodus wish.
If only I could find food in my way,
And it could be put in my dish.

Samuel grew in favor with the Lord,
He learned many skills here.
When people came, Samuel preached the Word,
He spoke the message so clear.

Elijah

I know a man who spoke God's word,
From his learnings and not a book.
If what he spoke caused fear and pain,
God told him to hide by a brook.

There I will feed you and give you drink,
I will have my birds drop on by.
I can do more than you think,
Remember the manna that came from the sky?

So Elijah went and dwelt by the brook,
He trusted the Lord to be nearby.
The birds brought him meat,
And were singing from on high.

After a while, the Lord told him to move,
To another city and another gate.
He saw a widow gathering sticks,
She would use to eat a meal very late.

Saying, this is for a meal
For my son and I to eat.
When we finish this,
There is no more meat.

Elijah said the barrel of meal shall never end,
There will be plenty for many days to eat.
This is what the Lord says to me,
In my ear the words are very sweet.

For you have been a blessing to me
Sharing with what little you had.
So the food you have will not run out,
For you and your wonderful lad.

Jehoshaphat

Was there ever a king like Jehoshaphat,
Who taught the law of the Lord?
Many people stepped on his welcome mat,
There was never any fear of a sword.

Many people brought him presents,
Even the mighty men of war,
Those who were city residents,
Even the Egyptians who were all on a tour.

Jehoshaphat put in the city judges,
He had them stand near the entrance gate.
They settled the many grudges,
And did not enter in a debate.

He heard of the great army coming his way,
He feared and trusted the Lord again.
"Let judgment fall from You today,
Let them see Your Mighty Hand."

The next morning, they marched out singing,
The Lord's Mercy to the end will endure.
Confusion in their head was ringing.
They destroyed themselves in this game of war.

Hezekiah

Come to the house of the Lord,
All you leaders of the land.
We will read from the Almighty Word,
And celebrate the Passover on our sand.

I'm sending this letter to you leaders,
We have not had a meeting for a while.
We must gather at my house for the seder,
It will be good to see your smile.

Those in Judah with one heart came together,
Hezekiah prayed for every leader.
Let us come to the house in any weather,
And bless now the Torah reader.

Bless the one who leads the singing,
Unites us together singing Praise.
Our voices to You are ringing,
And our hands to You we raise.

37

May we rejoice in Your Thanksgiving,
Your Praises lift our Spirits high.
May we exalt the One ever-living,
With our words to You we cry.

Ezra

Cyrus, the king, made a decree,
In building the Lord's house today.
To be bowing on your knee,
As to the Lord we seek and pray.

Whatever is written in the deed,
To build the house of the Lord today.
See if I have what you need,
Check with me, without delay.

The royal treasury will pay the cost,
So take whatever you need.
Build now, before time is lost,
And Haggai had instructions on the deed.

Our enemies don't want this rebuilt,
They discouraged us every day.
The right corner is in a tilt,
They told us we were shown the wrong way.

They sent a letter to the king,
The Jews are rebuilding the wall.
Let it be put on your ring,
They won't respect or call.

They never pay their tax,
Yet they use and abuse the land.
I don't think anything they lack,
Then they eat from our hand.

Please stop them from building,
And damaging our crops.
Stop them from using our fielding,
In hopes of these invaders you can stop.

Nehemiah

Into the king's presence I go each day,
Taking him drink and food.
Lately he knows how sad I've been,
He can tell because of my mood.

He said, "Nehemiah, what causes your grief?
I can see all your pain.
Maybe, Nehemiah, I can help,
And clear up some of your rain."

O King let it be known to you,
My city is in distress.
The walls are broken down,
And the mud in the road makes a mess.

All the bushes and trees are brown,
And the flowers have wilted away.
All the cattle and horses are thin,
Because there is no more hay.

Nehemiah, I want you to go and rebuild your city today.
I will request you have all the lumber you need.
I will get permission from the leaders of the land,
For you to carry out this wonderful deed.

Esther

I know the Lord has a plan for me,
I read it in His word.
I try to go where He leads,
Just like an Eagle who soars.

So when the way seems rough,
And things don't go as you plan.
The Lord takes hold of your cuff,
And He will lead you, just give Him your hand.

I couldn't reveal my race,
When I was chosen to be Queen.
I was the one giving the grace,
Over all those that were seen.

I had no mother or father,
Mordecai raised me as his own.
He taught me the Holy Scripture.
I memorized a lot as I've grown.

There was a man named Haman,
Who thought he deserved a bow.
He expected people to honor him,
Much like the holy cow.

Mordecai soon walked by,
Without a bow or bending the knee.
Haman was so furious,
He had the king make a decree.

That people must follow the laws,
If you are living on our land.
If you want to disobey,
Then get off our sand.

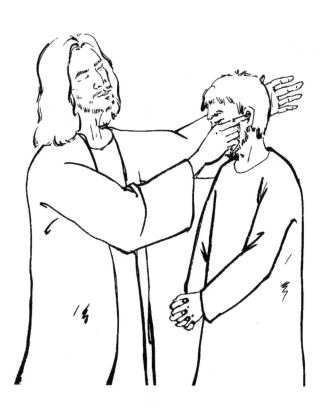

Isaiah

I saw the Lord high and lifted up,
His train filled the temple.
I reached out to take my cup,
A live coal was for my sup.

The mountain of the Lord,
Shall be above the hills.
There will be so many people there,
It will the entire place fill.

When the Lord shakes the earth,
They shall hide in the rocks.
But the Lord has every key,
Every place He can unlock.

People who have walked in darkness,
Will see a light that will not cease.
A son will be born,
Who is called, "The Prince of Peace."

A cow and a bear shall feed,
The wolf shall dwell with the lamb.
A calf will dwell with a lion,
A leopard will be with a ram.

As the waters cover the sea,
The earth shall be full of my name.
There will be no fighting here,
I will heal all the lame.

Trains Up In the Sky

Standing outside, I saw the sun,
As the birds went by, they crowed.
As the clouds connected one by one,
Just like an old railroad.

This train is coming, you can hear it now,
As the Lord cries out today.
Jump on board, get ready, get your heart in tune.
I am coming very soon!

The train is coming fast,
Over the hills and mountains today.
I thought I saw it pass,
Or did it go another way?

The train is coming soon.
Are you ready—did you read His word?
I hear the train whistling at noon,
The trains traveling fast I heard.

The Son is on His way,
He's traveling through thick and thin.
If He's coming back today,
Would you be ready with all your kin?

Jeremiah

There are things I must say to the nations,
There are things I must say soon.
If they don't turn from their idols,
I'm sending an enemy army at noon.

Who am I to speak those words?
Who will believe me when I do?
Let me be assured,
These words spoken are from you.

I knew you in the belly,
Before you were born.
I call you to speak my words,
From night to the early morn.

I'm calling you to be a Watchman,
To warn of the good and the bad.
And when you speak the warning,
The people will be very mad.

They don't want to obey me,
When I tell them the truth.
They want to keep gleaning wickedness,
Instead of obeying me like Ruth.

Lamentations

Leaves swirling in the wind,
Watching birds fly back and forth.
It is the time of year,
That birds fly to the north.

Watching early in the morn,
As a mother brings grass to her nest.
As she bends down to give the food,
You can see her colorful crest.

The Compassions of Our Lord never fail,
They are new every morning.
Just as the bird brings food to her young,
And flowers to the nest adorning.

He always lifts us up,
Out of the stormy way.
He sets our feet on solid ground,
Out of the scratchy hay.

Our persecutors are swifter than eagles,
They pursue us up the mountain.
In life we can trust the Lord to be,
Our ever-living fountain.

Ezekiel

I saw four wheels moving,
From side to side they went.
They all had faces and form,
And I wondered what all this meant.

Son of man, I'm sending you to Israel,
I want you to speak what I say.
They are a very rebellious house,
They are against Me to this day.

Speak to the mountains and valleys,
I will cast them all down.
Some will escape,
But most will wear a frown.

Do you see the man with the censer,
And the incense arising from his hand?
You wonder how much evil was accomplished,
All over the idol-bearing land.

I wanted to give them,

A land flowing with milk and honey.
They despised My ways,
And went after ways to make money.

I will set a Watchman for my people,
To warn the land.
When he sees the sword coming,
He'll warn them by his hand.

Do you see the dry bones in the valley?
Will they come to life soon?
It will take a lot of time,
Just like the butterfly and cocoon.

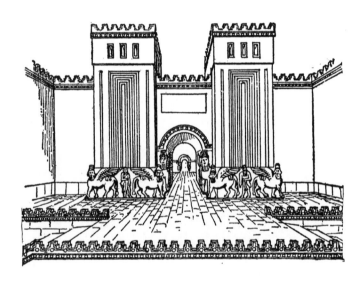

Daniel

Of the Children of Judah there was one,
Whom all wisdom and understanding had.
He was very skillful and wise,
Daniel was an amazing lad.

He was chosen to stand before the king,
To learn the language there.
He asked some of the food not to eat,
And still he had a face so fair.

Nebuchadnezzar had some troubling sleep,
He could not remember a dream.
He was so upset by this,
He called his astrologer team.

I have dreamed something in my sleep,
The remembrance of it won't come to me.
But if you show me what it was,
Many men to you will bow the knee.

Nebuchadnezzar, we do want to help,
Just tell us the vision you had.
If you do and let us advise,
You won't be so mad!

Daniel heard about the dream,
He went to the king and said,
"There is a God who knows everything,
This is the truth and it's what I have read."

"God has revealed to you secrets,
That will happen in the last days.
There will be a kingdom to come,
It will be partly iron mixed with clay."

Joel

The vine dries up,
The fig tree fails.
The day of the Lord is here,
The town crier hails!

The brooks are dried up,
The barns are torn down.
If you listen closely,
You can hear a Heavenly sound.

All the trees of the field are burned,
All the pastures are gone.
And the grass is no longer here,
On my big front lawn.

The Earth will quake before them.
The sun and moon will be dark.
All the trees are withered,
Because there is no more bark.

They shall run to and fro,
They shall run on the wall.
The Lord utters His voice,
Please hear Me when I call!

Turn to Me now,
Give Me your heart today.
And all the dark clouds you have,
Will turn to a sun ray.

Amos

A leader of sheep am I,

Out in the countryside.

I know all my sheep by name,

And they know me as their guide.

I try to avoid rock falls,

That come from the mountains so high,

So my sheep won't be distracted,

From what seems to come from the sky.

I take them around the lakes,

So they won't slip or fall in.

Every once in a while,

I see a great big fin.

I try to keep their path straight.

I try to give them a sign,

That their way must be on the path,

Measured straight like the plumb line.

Obadiah

Do you see the slaughter?
What about the destruction on that day?
The day strangers entered my land,
And took my captives away.

You should not have looked on the other side,
You should not have rejoiced in their distress.
When the enemies were fighting on the East,
You should not have stood in the West.

Have you said, in your heart,
As you stood in the cleft of the rock?
As an eagle, I'm flying high,
As time goes by on the clock.

You should not have ignored your brother,
In that day he became a stranger.
He had violence done to him,
He was in so much danger!

The day of the Lord is near,
It is soon coming to pass.
He will not forget what you have done,
Or the violence done to the mass.

Jonah

The word of the Lord came to Jonah,
He should be a witness to a city and go,
And share what the Torah says.
One who disobeys is a foe.

Jonah got on a ship to Tarshish,
He was on the ship to flee.
Instead of obeying the Lord,
He was instead thrown in the sea.

There was a great whale going by.
He moved his fins up and down,
As if to tell the other fish,
Don't come near my part of town.

Jonah saw him heading his way,
With his mouth open wide.
He thought, "Oh no, here I go,
For a big, gigantic ride."

Jonah slid all the way down his throat,
Into his stomach he went.
The water and weed swirled around him,
He stayed until he did repent.

The whale spit Jonah on dry land,
The Lord said, "Preach to Nineveh this time."
Jonah went saying, "Forty days you have to live."
The people said, "Lord, please forgive us for our crimes."

Micah

I am going to rain stones on Samaria,
I am going to burn Israel with fire.
They must get rid of their Idols,
That's what I hear from the town crier.

The mountains are molten in Jacob,
Samara is a heap in the field.
The plants are dry in the valley,
And what do your Vineyards yield?

I am going to send a ruler to Israel,
One that will bring healing to the land.
One who will perform miracles,
All with the touching of his hand.

The mountain of the house of the Lord,
Shall be exalted above the hills.
Many people will go and learn of his ways.
When they come down, they'll be overfilled,

With blessings from on high,
That reach down to the people below.
And when they see the gifts,
They're usually wrapped with a big white bow!

Nahum

Where is the dwelling of lions?
Where are they born?
Do I hear them crying?
Out in the early morn.

It might be in Nineveh.
It is empty, void and waste.
All the people traveled far,
They all left in their haste.

We used to ride chariots in the streets.
The Lord asking for repentance would call.
They ran so fast on their feet,
And in the streets, they would fall.

The Lord is Mighty and Grand,
He is very great in power.
If you give Him your hand,
Then you, like the cat, won't cower.

91

The Lord will give you fountains,
If you cut off the house of your gods.
Then He will send on the mountains,
The shepherds who carry the rods.

Habakkuk

The Sun and Moon Stood Still,
At the shining of the glittering spear.
The mountain saw the stars,
And they trembled and did fear.

The horses are swifter than leopards,
From far, their horsemen come.
They are flying so fast,
You can't even count the sum.

The Chaldeans are bitter nation,
That I will raise up today.
For judgment on the heathen,
And knowing this you will say.

I can't look on their evil,
There are so many of them.
Treacherous, they deal,
And they won't deal in gems.

Who builds a town with blood,
Iniquity is found there.
Put foundation on the stone,
You may find gems so rare.

If the Lord builds the town,
His knowledge will cover the Earth.
The trees with clap and sing,
As they all give new birth.

Zephaniah

When you stand in line to get your decree,
Are you thinking of times you read your book?
Are you thinking of time spent on your knee?
Or did this, you overlook?

The day of the Lord is near,
The day of the trumpet and the alarm.
It is a day of fear,
One that will cause you harm.

I will bring distress on men in that day,
Because they have walked blind.
Because they have gone their own way,
Without looking at the signs.

I will search with candles,
The hills and the gates.
Because they still walk in sandals,
They don't have an excuse for being late.

Hold your peace at my table,
I have summoned my guests.
I am not telling a fable,
The meat will be the very best!

For the Lord is in the midst of thee,
He will rejoice over you!
As you stand to get your decree,
He will have made all things new.

Haggai

Go up to the mountain,
Bring wood and come down.
Bring your gold and silver,
And build My Temple Mound.

Your house has many stones,
Your siding is blue.
Your grass in front is all brown,
Because the heaven has held her dew.

It's time to build my house.
It's time for people to come and give Glory.
It's time to come for peace,
And to hear our Creator's story.

We will obey the Lord,
Zerubbabel did say.
We will have it done,
In the latter house way.

Zerubbabel be strong,
We can build on the land.
I will give you all My strength,
So you can follow My Holy Plan.

Zechariah

I saw a man on a red horse,
He was among the myrtle trees.
He walked to and fro through all the Earth,
And it seems to be at ease.

I see a golden candlestick,
And on it were seven pipes.
There were trees surrounding this,
The olives on the tree were ripe.

What is this Vision, shown to me?
I just woke up this hour.
If you trust me to build your house,
Then you can know of my power.

Zerubbabel, is there a foundation on your house?
The Lord made Jerusalem without using walls.
You can have a perfect plan too,
If you follow My Foundation laws.

Not by might or power is the way they are built,
But according to My spirit that's in you.
If you follow My Foundation laws,
Then the heavens above shall give their due.

Malachi

What has been your offering?
Polluted bread on my altar.
I give you mountains and hills,
What has been your exchange barter?

I tell the sun to rise,
But you have brought it low.
I tell the Stars to shine,
And with the rain, there is a bow.

Your offering has a smell of smoke,
Is that what you call to rise?
Your offering is polluted,
Do you think it is very wise?

My Covenant is life and peace,
The law of truth is in his mouth.
Levi walked in all my ways,
He never thought of going south.

I am sending My messenger before you,
He shall prepare the way.
I will send My Covenant,
That he will prepare in that day.

Come and Dine

Come to my table,
I'm calling you now.
The utensils are set,
With a fork and a towel.

The food is ready,
For all to come and dine.
We're having grape juice,
I am the fruit of the vine.

Every place should be filled,
There is plenty to eat.
I've called many people,
To fill every seat.

Excuses I hear,
When it's soon time to eat.
"I must go to a game."
"I must get a good seat."

People's lives are too busy,
There's no time for me.
They're spending life going to and fro,
There's no time spent on the knee.

About the Author

Gina Woo is a mother from Pennsylvania. This is her first book of poetry. She has been writing poems since she was in grade school. She graduated from Valley Forge Bible College.

Made in the USA
Columbia, SC
19 October 2021

47506238R00070